William T. Goodman
& Robert W. Holmes

Atmospheric
FORGE &
HEAT TREAT
Oven

David J. Gingery Publishing LLC

ISBN 1-878087-28-2

Library of Congress Control Number: 2003112352

Printed in the United States Of America

Published by
David J. Gingery Publishing LLC
P.O. Box 318
Rogersville, MO 65742

Web: http://www.gingerybooks.com
Email: gingery@gingerybooks.com

Warning

There are serious hazards in the processes and procedures in this book. No attempt has been made to point out all of the dangers or even a majority of them. Be careful! Use good solid judgement in your work, and think ahead. David J. Gingery Publishing LLC has not built this project or tested the methods and procedures discribed. We hereby disclaim any liability for injury to persons or property that may result while using this book.

ACKNOWLEDGMENTS

I'd like to thank my friend, Bob Holmes, who has been a great source of encouragement and stability over the years. He has helped more than he will ever know. Between us, the forge has taken on a life of its own.

Many thanks to Mike Murphy, Bill Agee, and Dave Allen, especially Mike, who has really come through when needed as computers crashed, software glitches, and rational thoughts are needed just to figure out how to use the impossible things such as software.

Thanks to Edward Mitchell and Tom Green for getting David Gingery to visit our class and thus beginning the process of writing this book.

And many thanks to David Gingery, who after seeing the actual forge, convinced me to write this book. I'll try to do my best.

This book is dedicated to my son, Alex. It's fun to watch him grow.

SAFETY AND DISCLAIMER

➤ It is assumed that the reader has the necessary skills, experience, and understanding of materials and machine processes that are required to build this machine. Or the alternative, the reader has access to qualified individuals or metalworking businesses with people to do the processes that may be beyond the reader's ability to do safely.

➤ The directions contained in this book are proven to work as by the accompanying photos. Any deviation should be taken with great caution and safety.

➤ As the forge is built, note that the materials, metal and refractory, are of mass and weight and will gain weight as time and assembly goes on. When it comes time to lift the fire box to the top of the column or to move the assembled forge, please get help to do so.

➤ This machine burns propane and is designed to heat metal. Turn off valves when not in use. Be diligent in checking for leaks and promptly correct them as they may occur. Use the forge in a well ventilated area, and never leave it unattended while it is in use. Watch for hot metal and also watch out for others. Never let incompetent people use the forge or other tools unsupervised. Remember, all the reasonable safety rules that a blacksmith would adhere to apply here.

➤ Work in a clean uncluttered area. Insure the floor is clean from debris and items not necessary for the job at hand are out of the way. Make it a habit to practice clean and safe work habits always using the proper safety equipment that is in good condition, especially eye protection devices.

➤ Make sure all clamps are secure when in use and remove them when appropriate.

➤ There are many dangers both seen and unseen in this and any other project you are likely to encounter. Remember to be constantly alert, always using your best judgment in protecting yourself and others.

➤ The Forge is going to perform and look as best as you make it, so do your best. It will speak for you and about you for a long time.

Table Of Contents

Foreword

Like my own Charcoal Foundry and Gas Crucible Furnace, The Goodman/Holmes gas fired forge materialized in response to a personal need. Of course a "need" is in reality no more than a "want" driven by some extra passion. Often our fanciful needs are beyond our pocketbooks so that extra bit of passion drives us to discover ways to supply the need or devise some alternative to advance a project. This process of learning and developing skills requires research, study and copious notes and drawings. When we are successful the archives of our pursuit may become the outline for a manual that will enable others to duplicate our achievement. That is the common origin of how-to-books.

When I first saw the Goodman/Holmes forge I was impressed with its appearance. When it was fired and I saw it perform I was persuaded that it was a practical project for a how-to manual and I urged Bill and Bob to go for it. Fortunately notes and drawings had been kept so this book is their response. If you are working with metals you will eventually want to raise it to high temperatures to change its state, its shape or its degree of hardness. This piece of equipment will enable you to do it.

There are several unique features of this amazing piece of shop equipment. The most outstanding feature is the high output atmospheric burner. The cleverness of arranging twin flames that impinge on each other results in a single concentrated flame that raises temperature rapidly. But the radial holes that admit the extra primary air, thus eliminating the need for a blower, are the master stroke. You might even call it genius but I won't risk swelling any heads. It's just mighty good design and it works very well. There are other possible applications for this burner design, including metal melting and ceramics, so the details of the burner design alone make this book a bargain.

I'm pleased and proud that Bill and Bob responded to my suggestion.

Dave Gingery

6

Welcome! ... And thank you.

Bob and I appreciate you buying a copy of <u>Atmospheric Forge</u>. We hope you enjoy reading this missive as much as we enjoyed designing, building the Forge and writing about it.

A lot of time, energy, thinking and rethinking, and an incredible amount of experimentation went into this project. The original idea was developed about twenty years ago and it worked well. The later development you see detailed in this book is the result of practical use and recognition of needed changes over time. We feel certain you will recognize the ease of use,

enhanced safety, and ergonomic considerations of our experience.

To describe ourselves as our metal working background is long and varied. Bob Holmes is an Experimental Machinist with a state university and with over 27 years experience as a tool and die machinist in the aerospace industry prior to that. My background is a technologist (read machinist) for 25 years with the same university. For those of you who would inquire, a technologist is one who is heavily trained in metals, woods, electronics, plastics, and other mediums.

Bob and I have over 50 years experience between us in the problem solving field of creation of machines and processes. We bring varied and unique ways and opinions to this project.

So now the question - How did the Forge come about? One of my intense hobbies is blacksmithing. I have been doing blacksmithing since I was a teenager. One of my needs at the time was a small portable forge with an alternative fuel source other than coal. At the time coal was hard for me to get. I had built a small forge using kaowool, a heat resistant insulator used in the pottery making field. This early model was light, mobile, and of the bench top variety. It heated well to 1800 degrees and was suitable for 95% of the work I was doing. The other five percent usually involved forge welding and when that need arose, I often resorted to arc welding. So this small original model suited me well for over twenty years.

About 1995, Bob indicated he needed a heat treat oven to treat some small parts but noted there was no facility near by. We also found the cost to have someone else do our heat treating was prohibitive, as well as concerns of questionable quality of work, and the turnaround time involved seemed excessive too. So I introduced my small forge to him as a possible way of getting the job done. Bob liked the forge immediately, but noted improvements could be made. So working together, using each other as a sounding board, we fed ideas one to another, moving to the final design you see here in this book. We are happy to say that the forge/heat treat oven has exceeded all of our expectations and we feel it is an attractive, durable, multiusable machine that can be economically built in the average home shop.

After we built this machine, we gave one to a registered metallurgical engineer to test. It was really quite fun because the engineer refused to believe the machine would work even when we demonstrated it before his eyes. As we looked on, the forge reached 2500 degrees from a cold start in less than 2-1/2 minutes. He took the forge with him and continued to run tests and was amazed with the results. Later a similar forge was given to David Gingery.

The Facts Of The Case . . .

Why are we proud of this atmospheric forge? Let's list several reasons.

1. It's nice to look at. The forge has clean lines. Our efforts allow us to blend several mediums and methods of processes to produce a nice, professional looking piece of equipment. Following the directions of this manual will help you produce a quality looking machine that you will be proud to own.

2. It is economical to use. The forge will run on 1-1/2 pounds pressure to 1800 degrees. A 40 pound tank of propane should do two eight hour work days easily. A large upright propane cylinder should give you two weeks of continuous work at the minimum. I am not aware of any location that propane is not available. The by products of the forge are heat, water vapor and carbon monoxide. Carbon monoxide gas is deadly so unless you can provide ample ventilation, use the forge only outdoors.

3. The design allows for several possible situations. The large openings at either end permit work to be done at the same time or a long piece can be worked.

The Forge can be used by one person or several at the same time. Schools, blacksmith meetings, and other locations will find this useful. And the large opening allows for aluminum to be melted, so foundry work could easily be done as well.

4. The refractory material we used is designed to withstand 5000 degrees. There is about one inch or 25mm thickness throughout the interior of the forge firebox. The design is a six sided hexagon that aids in the circulation of gas within the firebox so dead spots are reduced. Every model that ran still maintained an exterior that was not hot to the touch.

5. Ergonomics. This machine design, as with any machine, has to be with the thought of use. If it is uncomfortable to use or causes back pain, then the user will not use the machine. Bob and I are of middle age and beyond. So our needs as well as yours regardless of age are of safety and of reducing the causes of physical stress. The door openings are about 48 to 50 inches from the floor to prevent bending over while looking into the forge. We have

experimented with a table model but still had to design a special stand to elevate the forge to a useful height. The feet ends are beveled back to reduce material to stand on. Handles are wooden and positioned away from the doors.

6. The two door openings on the forge are 6" x 6". Most work can be accommodated by the forge. But of course if you are heating a large mass of steel say a 4" cube, it may well take additional time and require special handling to extract and work.

7. The pyrometer is located just under one end of the fire chamber as you can see in the photo in figure 1. It is durable and has an easy to read analog dial. It has been enclosed in steel to reduce chances of damage and the thermocouple wire has been enclosed in steel conduit as well.

8. The Forge design is durable. The fire chamber is about 12" x 22". The steel surrounding the refractory is 1/4" thick and side walls are supported with expanded metal to allow for thermo expansion and contraction. Because of the hefty design, the forge can with stand serious abuse. Other than the doors and gas shut off valve, there are no moving parts.

9. It requires no electricity, is fully self contained and can go anywhere in the world and work.

10. It works. One of the demonstrations we do is place a beer bottle in the bottom of the fire chamber prior to firing the forge. In 25 seconds after firing, the bottle was all but a molten puddle of glass. This never fails to impress me.

11. It is quiet. Dave Gingery and I had a normal conversation while we demonstrated the model and he and I are both hard of hearing, but we did fine that day.

12. It's a unique conversation piece. When showing the forge to "Metal Experts" a strange type of conversation occurs. First you get a "What in the @#&& is that!" Then long periods of silence punctuated with occasional words of "no-way, astounding, incredible, unbelievable, impossible," or similar types of words. Then out comes the measuring tapes to try to figure out what was done.

13. The numerous tests that were done on the forge show that it will go from a cold start to 2500 degrees in about two minutes. By anyone's standard, this is impressive.

Basic Parts Of The Forge

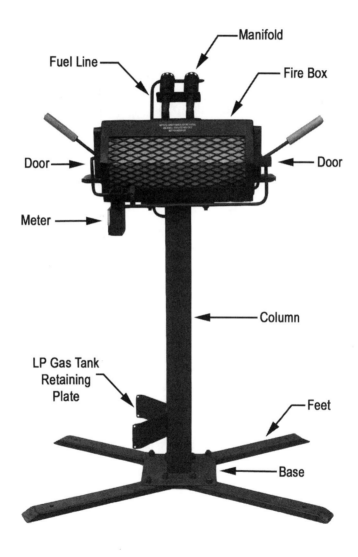

Figure 1.

List of materials

If you have trouble making any of the steel parts listed below, or have difficulty in locating material and supplies, we have numerous parts stored away including the 5000 deg.f. refractory suggested in this project. Please send a self addressed stamped envelope or international postal coupons to **Ozark Machine Systems, Box 4608 Glenstone Station, Springfield, Missouri, 65808**. Bob will send you the price and availability of the part, as well as the cost of shipping and handling.

As you can see from the photo on page 11, the forge is constructed of heavy steel. The required steel items can be cut to size and formed by the steel supply house, but using this approach can be expensive. So depending on how your shop is set up to handle such items, you might consider the purchase of drops and if possible cut, form or weld to size and shape yourself. The best place to look for drops is at the steel yard or metal scrap yard. Drops are the short ended pieces that companies often have left over from other jobs. They really can't be used on current jobs so they are often happy to sell them to you at greatly reduced prices. The main thing to avoid at the steel yard are the cut off fees. This is the fee they charge to cut steel to length. Often these charges total more than the cost of the material itself. If you find a piece longer than what you need, consider buying the whole thing and if possible cutting it to length yourself. Add what's left to your own scrap pile for the next project.

A term you will see referred to through out the text is "hot roll steel" abbreviated h.r.s. The term hot rolled steel refers to the way the steel was processed. Hot roll steel has a surface finish that tends to be rough and scaly and is much cheaper to buy than its cousin cold rolled steel. Cold rolled steel on the other hand has a smooth finish and is accurate to .003 - .005" when it leaves the mill. For this project we do not need anything as exacting as c.r.s. so h.r.s suggested.

Another item used in this project that needs special mention is insulating refractory cement. Refractory is a cement like material specially formulated to withstand high temperature and

12

it usually comes in 50 pound bags. The refractory we used is rated at 5000 degrees Fahrenheit. If you have difficulty finding 5000 degree refractory, 3000 degree will work. Be aware though that 3000 degree refractory will likely wear at a faster rate. You won't find refractory at the local hardware store or lumber yard. But pottery supply dealers often sell refractory. Just look in the yellow pages under pottery suppliers or run a search on the internet. Two internet suppliers are. . .

http://www.mcmastercarr.com
http://www.budgetcastingsupply.com.

A pyrometer is also mentioned in the material list as an item you will need if you decide to use the machine as a heat treat oven. Pottery suppliers will stock this item as well. Expect to spend between $75.00 and $100.00. The pyrometer comes with a thermocouple and the necessary wire to connect it to the meter. Thermocouples come in varying lengths and you will need one that is 12" long. Your pyrometer should also come with wiring instructions, but if not, the following will generally apply. The read lead of a thermocouple or wire is the negative or magnetic lead. The yellow lead is the positive lead. By using a magnet you can always make certain that your thermocouple is correctly installed. If your meter is wired in reverse it will not work. Not to worry though, just switching the wires on one end should fix it. If you are unable to find a supplier locally, run an internet search. As I was compiling this book, I found three suppliers in just a few minutes using the YAHOO search engine.

They were. . .

http:///www.baileypottery.com
http://www.axner.com
http://www.artclay.com

The copper fittings used for the manifold are of a larger size than will be found at most hardware and building supply stores. So purchasing these items may require a visit to a plumbing supply dealer.

And now for the individual parts list. . .

Column and feet

Four, 1" x 4" x 24" lengths of 3/16" wall steel tubing. These are for the feet. See figure 2.

One, 12" x 12" piece of h.r.s. plate. Base plate. See figure 3.

One, 4" x 4" x 48" piece of 1/4" wall h.r.s. square tubing. Column. See figure 4.

One, 5" x 11" piece of 1/4" h.r.s.. Top column plate. See figure 9.

Eight, 5/8 – 11 threaded stud bolts 2-1/2" long, ends chamfered, cut from a length of all thread rod along with the same number of 5/8-11nuts and lock washers. To fasten the feet to the base plate. Figure 6.

One 4" x 19" piece of 3/16" h.r.s.. LP gas retainer plate. See figure 8.

Four 1/2" O.D. x 1" long pieces of steel tubing. Support inserts for the feet. See figure 2.

Basic firebox

Two pieces of 1/4" x 10-1/4" x 22" h.r.s.. Top & bottom fire box plates. See figures 10 and 11.

Two pieces of 12" x 22" expanded metal, your choice. Recommend 1/8" thick. See figure 14.

Four pieces of 5/8 -11 all thread, 2-1/2" long with four 5/8-11nuts with lock washers. Studs for bottom fire box plate. Used to attach fire box to top column plate. See figure 10.

Refractory

Three to four bags, of insulating refractory cement. 5000 degree F. suggested, but 3000 degree F. temperature rating will work. Bob & I have a quantity of 5000 degree refractory in stock. Refer to the first paragraph on page 12 for further information.

End plates

Two 11-3/4" x 13" pieces of 1/4" h.r.s.. End plates. See figure 26.

Two 2" x 3" x 6" pieces of 1/4" h.r.s. angle. Angle shelf. See figure 27.

Doors

Two 7-1/8" x 7-1/8" pieces of 1/8" h.r.s. Door blanks. See figure 35.

Two 28" long pieces of 1/8" x 1" band steel. Door sides. See figure 36 and 37.

Two pieces of 1" x 1" x 1/8" h.r.s. angle 4" long. To support door refractory. See figure 37.

Two pieces of 1/2" diameter x 28" h.r.s. round rod. Door handles. See figure 41 & 42.

Two pieces of 3" channel 1" long. Door hinges. See figure 39.

Two steel compression springs, 1/8" x 1/2" I.D. x 2" long. For door hinge. See figure 47.

Two roll pins 1/8" O.D. by one inch long. Door hinge assembly. See figure 47.

Two flat washers with 1/2" hole. Door hinge assembly. See figure 47.

One 3" x 3" piece of 3/4" h.r.s. plate. Door stop. See figure 46.

Four flat washers with 3/8" holes. To secure wooden handle. See figure 44.

Two 1/4" retainer rings. To secure wooden handle. See figure 44.

Two 1-1/4" diameter x 6" long hardwood dowels. Door handles. See figure 43.

Pyrometer, thermocouple & their housings

Purchase your desired meter and thermocouple from a pottery/ kiln supply house and note the dimensions. See figure 49 & 50.

One piece 5" channel 5" long. Pyrometer housing. See figure 56. The size of this item may vary depending on the size of your pyrometer.

One, 1-1/2" x 1-1/2" x 2-1/2" long piece of 1/8" wall tubing. Thermocouple housing. The size of this item may also vary depending on the size of the ceramic end of your thermocouple. See figure 51.

One piece of 1/2" O.D. x 30" thin wall steel tubing. Conduit to enclose wire from thermocouple to pyrometer. See figure 58.

One, 1/4-20 x 3/4" set screw. See figure 61.

Wood parts

One piece of 12" x 28" plywood 3/4" thick for the firebox interior side refractory panel mold. See figure 18.

Five feet of 1 x 2" wooden strips. For refractory panel mold. See figure 18.

Two 6" x 12" x 3/4" thick boards for the firebox alignment jig. See figure 16.

Two 4" hinges for firebox alignment jig. See figure 16.

One 9-1/2" x 9-1/2" board 3/4" thick for the refractory shelf mold. See figure 32.

3/8" x 1-1/2" wooden strips 32" long for shelf refractory mold. See figure 32.

One 6-7/16" x 6-3/8" x 3" wooden block to be used as a plug when casting fire box ends. See figure 33.

One, 1-3/8" dia. x 3-1/2" long round wood dowel to make two tapered plugs for firebox nozzle holes. See figure 24.

One 7/8" dia. x 8" long round wood dowel to make four firebox vent plugs and one thermocouple plug. See figure 24 and figure 34.

16

The manifold

Copper items listed below may be obtained from a plumbing supply dealer.

Two, 2-1/8" I.D. x 3" long copper unions. Manifold heads. See figure 68.

Two, 2" to 1" copper reducers. See figures 70 through 72.

Two 1", 45 degree copper elbows. See figure 78.

Four pieces of 1" x 3" long copper tubing. See figures 76-78.

One piece of 3/16" x 2" x 6-3/4" h.r.s.. Brace plate. See figure 64.

One piece of 3/16" x 3-1/2" x 7" h.r.s.. Base plate. See figure 65.

One piece of 1/2" O.D. x 48" long thin wall steel or copper tubing. Fuel line. See figure 81.

Propane tank, shut off valve, regulator and miscellaneous fittings and hose to connect the listed items to the fuel line. Figure 88. Note: If you use the unit as a heat treat oven you will need an adjustable regulator and pressure gage. See figures 89-91.

Column And Feet. . .

You will need to make four feet for the forge and each foot is made from a 1" x 4" x 24" long piece of 3/16" wall h.r.s. rectangular tubing. See figure 2 for details. Drill and tap the two 5/8 x 11 holes where shown. Note that the above mentioned holes will have to align with the 5/8" clearance

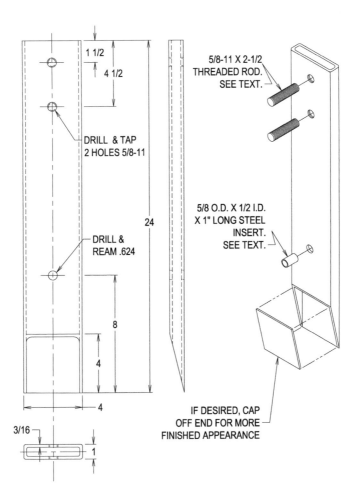

Figure 2. Forge foot. Make 4 from 1" x 4" x 3/16" wall h.r.s. tubing. **NOTE:** 5/8"-11 holes must align with the holes in the column base plate.

holes in the column base plate that we will be making next. Cut eight pieces of 5/8-11 all thread rod 2-1/2" long. Chamfer the ends and thread two into each foot as shown in the drawing. Tack weld each stud on the bottom to secure, and grind flush.

On the other end of each foot cut a bevel back 4 inches from the end. For a more finished appearance consider welding a piece of scrap plate on the beveled end of each foot and grind flush.

Eight inches from the beveled end and on center, drill and ream .624 for a press fit for the 1/2" I.D. x 1" long tube insert as shown in the drawing. This will enable the finished forge to be bolted down for safety and the steel insert will prevent the square tubing from collapsing when tightening the hold down bolts.

Make the column base plate from a piece of 3/8" thick h.r.s. cut 12" x 12" inches as shown in figure 3. Debur the edges and drill 5/8" clearance holes where shown. Care should be taken to insure the two holes on each corner align with the 5/8 studs on the feet. The overall footprint or area that will be covered by the base and feet is 32" x 48".

The column is made from a 4' long piece of 4" x 4" x 1/4" wall square tubing as shown in figure 4.

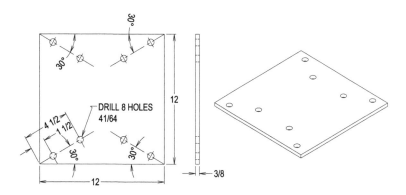

Figure 3. Base plate. Dimensions for hole locations are the same at all four corners. It is suggested that the plate be made of 3/8" thick h.r.s., but 1/4" will work. **Note:** Take care to ensure that the holes in the base plate align with the mounting studs on the feet.

Ensure both ends are square. To check for squareness, you can use a combination square or stand the column on end on a known flat surface and check all sides with a carpenter's level. Reverse the ends and repeat. After you are satisfied that both ends are square, proceed with attaching the column to the base plate. The easiest way to do this would be to simply weld the column to the center of the base plate and that's what we recommend. But you may

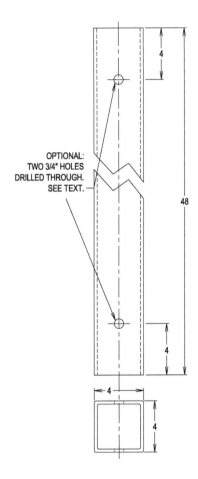

Figure 4. Column. Make one from 4" x 4" x 1/4" wall square tubing.

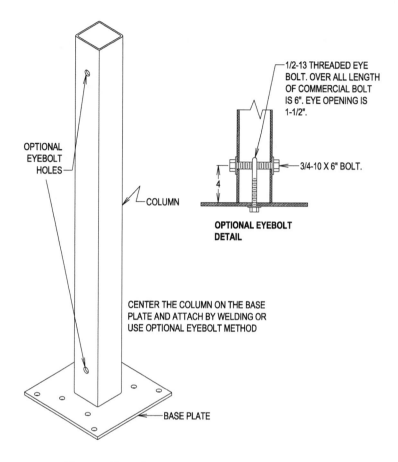

OPTIONAL
EYEBOLT
HOLES

COLUMN

1/2-13 THREADED EYE
BOLT. OVER ALL LENGTH
OF COMMERCIAL BOLT
IS 6". EYE OPENING IS
1-1/2".

3/4-10 X 6" BOLT.

4

**OPTIONAL EYEBOLT
DETAIL**

CENTER THE COLUMN ON THE BASE
PLATE AND ATTACH BY WELDING OR
USE OPTIONAL EYEBOLT METHOD

BASE PLATE

Figure 5. Detail for attaching the column to the base plate.

want to take the forge apart for transportation from time to time. With that in mind you might consider the optional eyebolt method as detailed in the upper right corner of figure 5.

When welding the column to the base, there is a danger the base will warp. A solid weld would definitely cause distortion so 2" weld beads on each of all four sides are adequate.

Fasten the feet to the column base plate with 5/8-11 nuts and lock washers as shown in figure 6.

Now with the column fastened to the base plate, you

21

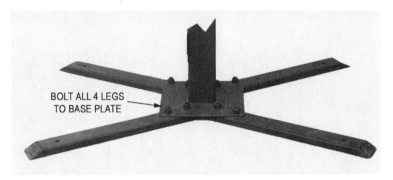

Figure 6. Bolt all 4 legs to base plate using 5/8-11 nuts with lock washers.

are ready to make the LP Gas retainer plate. Its function will be to secure the propane tank to the column. The detail is shown in figure 7 & 8 and it is made from a piece of 4" x 19" x 3/16" thick h.r.s.. Drill holes where shown and bend to shape. Radius the corners and deburr all edges. Tack weld the completed retainer plate to the column at 12" from floor

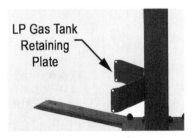

LP Gas Tank
Retaining
Plate

Figure 7. Detail showing postition of LP gas tank retaining plate.

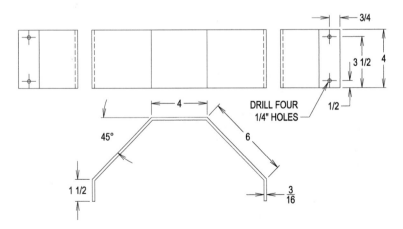

Figure 8. LP gas retainer plate. Make one from a piece of 4" x 19" x 3/16" h.r.s..

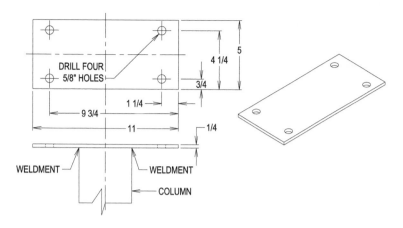

Figure 9. *Top column plate. Make one from 1/4" h.r.s. flat bar.*

level or center it at that point where the center of the propane tank corresponds with the column.

Next, make the column top plate from a piece of 5" x 11" h.r.s 1/4" thick. Refer to the drawing in figure 9. Drill 5/8" clearance holes where shown in the drawing. Place on top of the column and orient the long length of the top plate with the long length of the footprint of the feet. Center and check for squareness, then either weld as with the bottom base plate or attach using the eyebolt method.

At this point clean up the column, grind any sharp areas, and tighten the stud bolts. Check for any imperfections and correct and then paint. We used flat black paint.

Basic Firebox

This section covers the basic firebox construction. It includes shearing, sizing, machining, and some assembly.

The drawings in figures 10 and 11 show the top and bottom plates for the fire box. Each plate is made from 1/4" h.r.s. 10-1/4" wide x 22" long. The 60 degree bends on the 1/4" plate will present a problem for most home shops. You could have a sheet metal

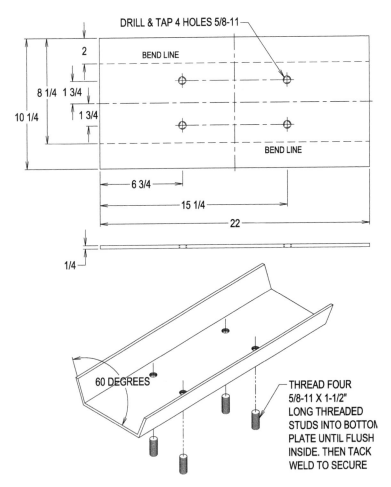

Figure 10. Fire box bottom plate. Make one from 1/4" h.r.s.

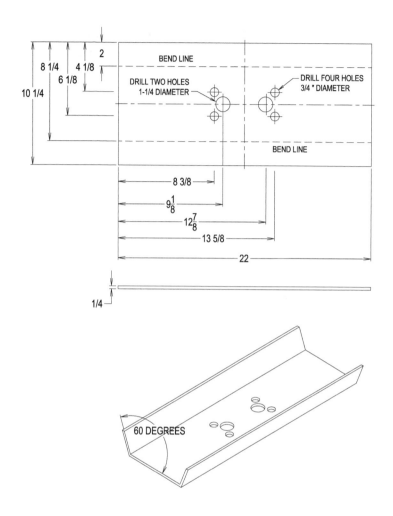

Figure 11. *Fire box top plate. Make one from 1/4" h.r.s.*

company make the bends or you could weld as an alternative. Figure 12 shows a couple of welding options and if you do decide to assemble the plates by welding, watch for distortion. Rather than welding down the entire length, lay short 2" welds spaced 2" or 3" apart.

Locate, drill and tap the four holes tapped 5/8-11 in the bottom plate. These holes must align with the holes in the top column plate in figure 9. When alignment has been

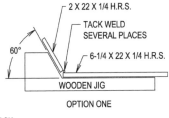

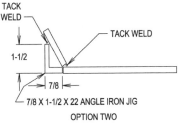

Figure 12. *Suggested alternative methods for making top & bottom fire box plates.*

verified, insert a 5/8-11 x 1-1/2" bolt stud in each hole and tack weld to secure.

Locate and drill the 3/4" vent holes and the 1-1/4" manifold nozzle holes in the top plate where shown. These holes will need to align with the holes in the manifold base plate shown in figure 65. It is likely that you will not have large enough drills to drill the holes in the top plate. As an alternative you could use a good quality holesaw at a low rpm Be sure and lubricate

with lots of oil as it cuts. When done, debur all sharp edges.

Next you will need two pieces of 1/8" thick expanded metal measuring 12" x 22" as shown in figure 14.

Now you fasten the top and bottom firebox plates to the expanded metal. It is best to use a couple jigs to align the pieces before welding the expanded metal to the plates. The jig detail can be found in figures 16 and 17. To accomplish the task, place one jig at each end of the plates with the hinge side facing outward. Assemble the top and bottom firebox plates and the expanded metal with clamps such as shown in figure 15. When all pieces are clamped together tack weld to secure.

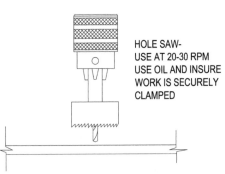

Figure 13. *A holesaw may be used to drill the larger holes.*

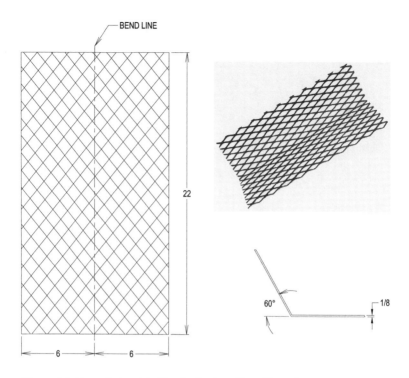

Figure 14. Expanded metal sides for fire box. You will need two pieces.

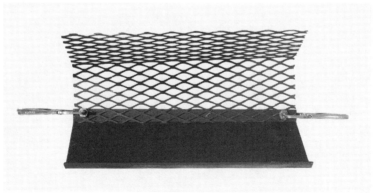

Figure 15. An example of clamps that can be used to secure the expanded metal to the top and bottom fire box plates.

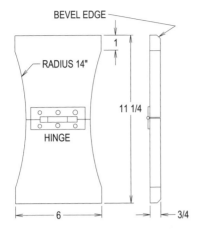

BEVEL EDGE

RADIUS 14"

1

11 1/4

HINGE

6

3/4

Or you may drill and tap, using fender washers and bolts. When assembly is complete, remove the jigs by pushing inwards on the hinges causing them to collapse for easy removal. Clean and paint the firebox as desired then set aside for later assembly.

Figure 16. Jig detail for fire box ends. These are made of wood and you will need two.

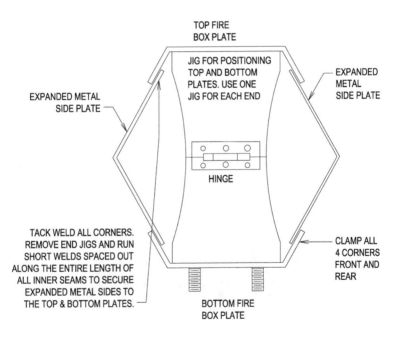

TOP FIRE
BOX PLATE

JIG FOR POSITIONING
TOP AND BOTTOM
PLATES. USE ONE
JIG FOR EACH END

EXPANDED
METAL
SIDE PLATE

EXPANDED METAL
SIDE PLATE

HINGE

TACK WELD ALL CORNERS.
REMOVE END JIGS AND RUN
SHORT WELDS SPACED OUT
ALONG THE ENTIRE LENGTH OF
ALL INNER SEAMS TO SECURE
EXPANDED METAL SIDES TO
THE TOP & BOTTOM PLATES.

CLAMP ALL
4 CORNERS
FRONT AND
REAR

BOTTOM FIRE
BOX PLATE

Figure 17. Assembling the fire box

Refractory castings

Now we come to one of the more interesting parts of the building of the forge and that is casting the refractory. We will start with the refractory castings for the side walls. And for that you will need to build a mold as shown in figure 18. You will need four identical castings. Since the drying time for each casting is 24 hours you could get the job done faster if you were to build four molds instead of just one. So with one mold for casting this part of the process would take four days. With four molds just one day.

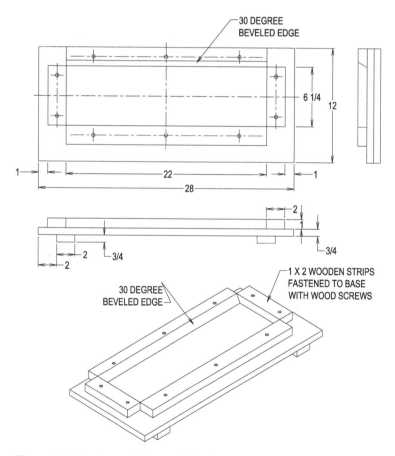

Figure 18. Refractory mold for producing the side walls in the fire box.

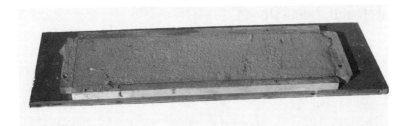

Figure 19. Lay refractory in the mold. strike off level and allow to set for 24 hours.

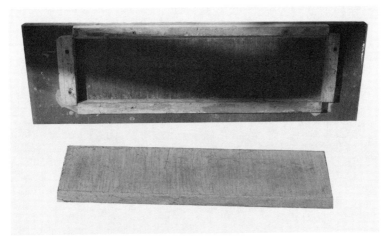

Figure 20. Here is the newly formed side wall piece.

Figure 21. End view of side wall showing 30 degree edge.

When you build the mold, remember to make one long edge 30 degrees. You will be mating two cast pieces together at the 30 degree side to make a 60 degree angle. The mold is designed to come apart by removing wood screws. Coating the inside surface of the mold with petroleum jelly for a mold release will make removal of the castings a bit easier. Follow the mixing directions for your refractory. Then fill the mold with the mix and strike off level. Allow to set for 24 hours. As mentioned earlier, you will need to make four cast panels.

Referring to figure 22, clamp the four cast panels as shown taking care to mate the beveled 30 degree edges together.

Place the assembled firebox on a flat wooden surface larger than the firebox plate. Build two wood dams 1-1/4" high and place at each end of the fire box plate as shown in figure 23. Lay mixed refractory in bottom of the fire

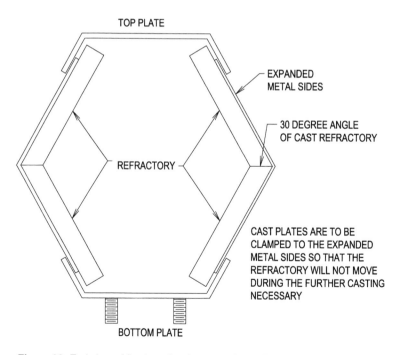

Figure 22. *End view of fire box showing cast plates clamped in position.*

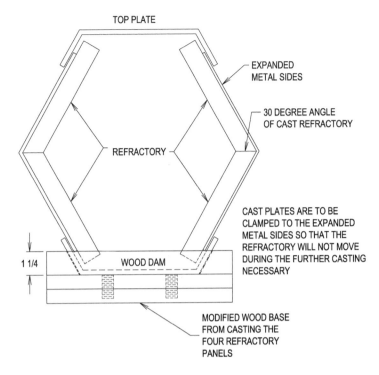

TOP PLATE

EXPANDED
METAL SIDES

30 DEGREE ANGLE
OF CAST REFRACTORY

REFRACTORY

CAST PLATES ARE TO BE
CLAMPED TO THE EXPANDED
METAL SIDES SO THAT THE
REFRACTORY WILL NOT MOVE
DURING THE FURTHER CASTING
NECESSARY

1 1/4

WOOD DAM

MODIFIED WOOD BASE
FROM CASTING THE
FOUR REFRACTORY
PANELS

Figure 23. Set up for pouring refractory in the bottom section of the fire box.

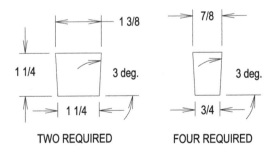

1 3/8   7/8

1 1/4   3 deg.   3 deg.

1 1/4   3/4

TWO REQUIRED   FOUR REQUIRED

Figure 24. Wooden plugs used to form the four vent holes in the top fire box refractory and the two manifold nozzle holes. See text.

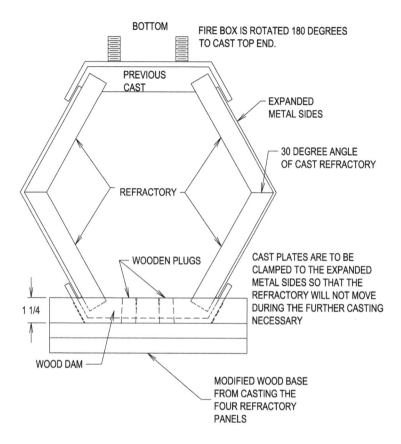

BOTTOM

FIRE BOX IS ROTATED 180 DEGREES
TO CAST TOP END.

PREVIOUS
CAST

EXPANDED
METAL SIDES

30 DEGREE ANGLE
OF CAST REFRACTORY

REFRACTORY

WOODEN PLUGS

CAST PLATES ARE TO BE
CLAMPED TO THE EXPANDED
METAL SIDES SO THAT THE
REFRACTORY WILL NOT MOVE
DURING THE FURTHER CASTING
NECESSARY

1 1/4

WOOD DAM

MODIFIED WOOD BASE
FROM CASTING THE
FOUR REFRACTORY
PANELS

Figure 25. *Set up for pouring refractory in the top section of the fire box.*

box strike of level to a depth of 1" and allow to set for 24 hours.

Rotate firebox 180 degrees and follow the same procedure to lay refractory in the top of the firebox. But before doing so, you will need to make casting plugs for the two nozzle holes and the four vent holes as shown in figure 24.

Insert a plug in each of all six holes. Apply petroleum jelly as a release agent. With wood dams in position, lay refractory to a depth of 1". Insure refractory is packed well around the plugs. Allow the refractory to set for 24 hours and then remove the wooden plugs. Set aside for next assembly.

End plate construction

The next step is to construct end plates, two are required.

The plates can be made from hot rolled steel that is either 3/16" or 1/4" thick. Ours were milled but they can

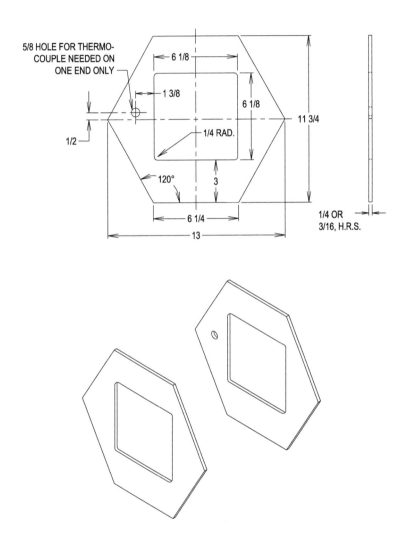

Figure 26. Fire box end plates. Make 2 from 3/16" or 1/4" h.r.s.

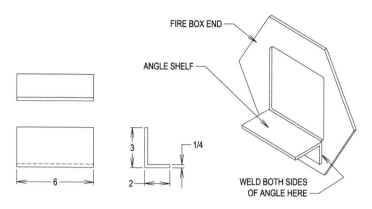

FIRE BOX END

ANGLE SHELF

3

1/4

6

2

WELD BOTH SIDES
OF ANGLE HERE

Figure 27. Detail showing angle shelf.

be sheared or flame cut. The inside openings are 6-1/8" square with radius corners. Make sure these openings have at least one inch distance from any edge. One of these plates will have a hole drilled to receive the thermocouple if later should you decide to use one. It is best to purchase the pyrometer and thermocouple now as the size of what you actually get will determine the later dimensions. We went to a pottery supply house and purchased a thermocouple and pyrometer for kilns. It was relatively inexpensive and durable. A simple analog meter will do, you can go digital if you prefer. The cost will only increase and electronics can fail. Or if you do not intend to use the forge as a heat treat oven you can do without.

Figure 28. Here the angle shelf is clamped to the end plate and ready for welding.

Cut two pieces of 1/4" h.r.s. angle 2" x 3" x 6". Square the ends and clamp flush to the bottom of the openings on each plate. Make sure that the two inch side is next to the plate and weld as shown in figure 27. Complete the same procedure to the other end plate.

After welding the angles to the end plates, you are now

35

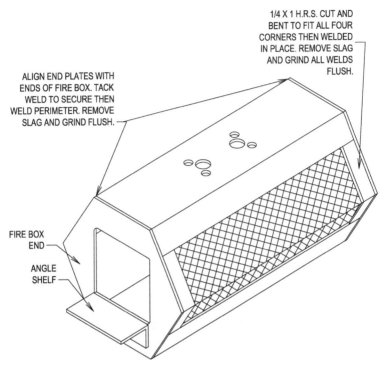

ALIGN END PLATES WITH
ENDS OF FIRE BOX. TACK
WELD TO SECURE THEN
WELD PERIMETER. REMOVE
SLAG AND GRIND FLUSH.

1/4 X 1 H.R.S. CUT AND
BENT TO FIT ALL FOUR
CORNERS THEN WELDED
IN PLACE. REMOVE SLAG
AND GRIND ALL WELDS
FLUSH.

FIRE BOX
END

ANGLE
SHELF

Figure 29. Asssembling the fire box.

ready to tack weld the end plates to the fire box. End plates are positioned at each end of the fire box as shown in figure 29. Align all edges and use a bar clamp to hold in position while you tack weld in several places. If you have difficulty in mating the end plate to the firebox, a large hammer might be used to persuade the end plate to mate properly. Finally, weld the entire seam at both ends of the fire box with a filler electrode such as an E7024 rod. This rod is a horizontal rod that fills gaps quite nicely. As you weld, remove any slag material, weld over the first weld, and bring up the bead to be slightly over. Then grind down smooth and radius the bead. This procedure is important as it presents the finished look that will speak of you when you show the machine. The neater and cleaner the machine looks, so do you.

The next procedure is to cut to fit 3/16" or 1/4" thick x 1" wide strips of h.r.s. to fit the four corners of the firebox as shown in figure 29. The 1" strips are bent at the 60 degree angle and are placed over the expanded metal at the corners. When positioned, weld the seams of each piece where they butt up to the end plate and the top and bottom plates. Then grind flush for a neat appearance.

SHELF
REFRACTORY

Figure 30.

The shelf refractory

Now we are ready to make the shelf refractory. The shelf refractory mold is shown in figure 32. A drawing of the finished refractory piece is shown in figure 31. The half circle indentions in each side of the refractory piece allow the refractory to fit within the door opening itself. When cast, the refractory shelf will sit on the shelf about 1/2" inside the fire box and parallel to the bottom.

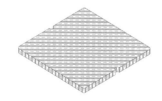

Figure 31. This drawing shows the finished shape of the shelf refractory.

37

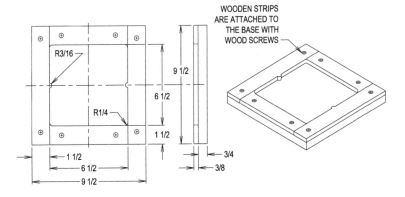

Figure 32. Shelf refractory mold.

Casting the firebox ends

In order to cast the fire box ends you will need two wooden plugs as shown in figure 33. One for each end. The flat side of each plug will be placed against the shelf refractory. The other three sides are tapered to allow later removal.

The plug is inserted into the door opening with the shelf refractory in place. The plug needs to extend at least one inch into the firebox to allow adequate refractory on the ends. So the tapered sides of the plug may need to be resized to fit the opening properly. A wood plug will also need to be made for the thermocouple. About 1-1/2" long will be adequate.

Doing one end at a time, place one of the shelf refractory on a shelf. If doing the thermocouple end first, place its plug in the hole. Be sure to apply liberal petroleum jelly for easy removal later. Coat the large wood plug with petroleum jelly and insert it in the door opening With every thing in place, stand the fire box on end, wood plug down, perhaps placing on wood 2 x 4's for stability. See figure 34. Mix and lay refractory into the end. Use a wide blade putty knife to help push wet refractory around the plug and next to the existing refractory side wall. Smooth out and make sure the refractory depth is at least 1". Wait 24 hours to

38

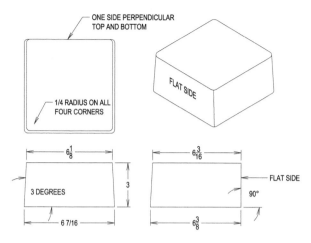

ONE SIDE PERPENDICULAR
TOP AND BOTTOM

FLAT SIDE

1/4 RADIUS ON ALL
FOUR CORNERS

$6\frac{1}{8}$

$6\frac{3}{16}$

FLAT SIDE

3 DEGREES

3

90°

6 7/16

$6\frac{3}{8}$

Figure 33. *Wooden plug to be used when casting fire box ends.*

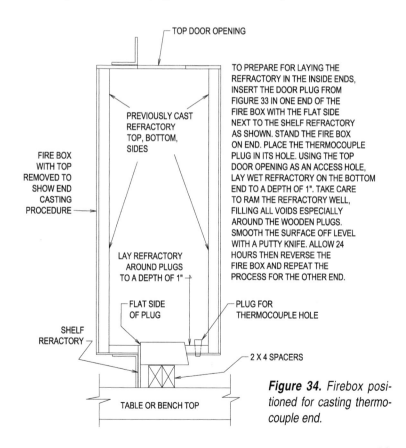

TOP DOOR OPENING

PREVIOUSLY CAST
REFRACTORY
TOP, BOTTOM,
SIDES

FIRE BOX
WITH TOP
REMOVED TO
SHOW END
CASTING
PROCEDURE

LAY REFRACTORY
AROUND PLUGS
TO A DEPTH OF 1"

FLAT SIDE
OF PLUG

PLUG FOR
THERMOCOUPLE HOLE

SHELF
RERACTORY

2 X 4 SPACERS

TABLE OR BENCH TOP

TO PREPARE FOR LAYING THE
REFRACTORY IN THE INSIDE ENDS,
INSERT THE DOOR PLUG FROM
FIGURE 33 IN ONE END OF THE
FIRE BOX WITH THE FLAT SIDE
NEXT TO THE SHELF REFRACTORY
AS SHOWN. STAND THE FIRE BOX
ON END. PLACE THE THERMOCOUPLE
PLUG IN ITS HOLE. USING THE TOP
DOOR OPENING AS AN ACCESS HOLE,
LAY WET REFRACTORY ON THE BOTTOM
END TO A DEPTH OF 1". TAKE CARE
TO RAM THE REFRACTORY WELL,
FILLING ALL VOIDS ESPECIALLY
AROUND THE WOODEN PLUGS.
SMOOTH THE SURFACE OFF LEVEL
WITH A PUTTY KNIFE. ALLOW 24
HOURS THEN REVERSE THE
FIRE BOX AND REPEAT THE
PROCESS FOR THE OTHER END.

Figure 34. *Firebox positioned for casting thermocouple end.*

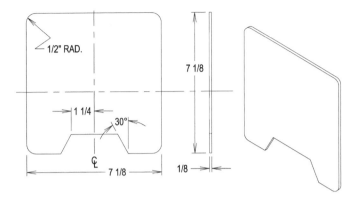

Figure 35. Door blanks. Make 1 for each end of the fire box from 1/8" h.r.s.

dry. After the refractory is completely dry, place firebox on its bottom and knock out the wooden plugs.

Repeat the process for the opposite end. Wait 24 hours for the refractory to set then place the fire box on its bottom and remove the plug. With both ends completed, you are ready to move on to the next step.

Door construction

Now for the doors. Two are required. Each is made from 1/8" thick h.r.s. cut 7-1/8" square or 1/2" larger than the openings in your fire box. See figure 35. Cut or grind a 1/2" radius on all four corners. The bottom cut out shown in each door serves as a vent opening and can also be used to heat items such as rods without having to open the doors.

Prepare the door blank for the refractory casting by cutting two pieces (one for each door) of 1/8" x 1" band steel 28" long and form it to fit the perimeter of each door

Figure 36. Photo of a finished door ready for the refractory.

40

blank as shown in figure 36 and 37. Tack weld in several places along the inside seam to secure. Each door is lined with 1" thick refractory and the strap metal serves to retain the refractory while casting. It will also continue to protect the refractory ends when the door is in use.

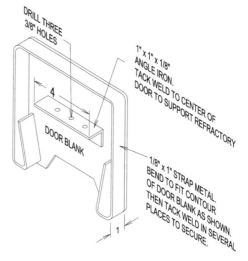

Figure 37. *Tack weld door edging around the perimeter of the door blank. Also tack weld the 4" long piece of angle in the center to support the refractory lining.*

The refractory will adhere to the door much better if it has something to grip to. A piece of 1" x 1" x 1/8" angle 4" long with 3/8" holes drilled in one side and then tack welded to the center surface of the door blank as shown in figure 37 will serve the purpose.

Lay the doors on a flat wood surface. Prepare a wood block for each door 1-1/8" thick and cut to fit into the vent opening to close the mold. The blocks can be secured to the wood base with screws. See figure 38. Mix refractory and poor inside both of the doors, strike off level and let dry 24 hours.

WOOD BLOCKS
TO CLOSE MOLD

Figure 38. *Casting the doors.*

Door hinge assembly

Begin by making the two door hinges. Each hinge being a 1" length of 3" h.r.s. channel. Drill a 9/16" diameter hole through each end of the hinges as shown in figure 39.

Next, weld one hinge on the lower right side of each end of the fire box as shown in figure 40. As you can see from the photo, hinges are positioned one inch from the end and aligned with the top edge of the lower base plate.

The metal door rods are the next item to make and are shown in figure 41 and 42.

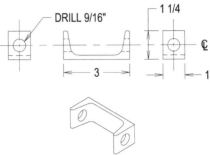

Figure 39. Door hinge. Make 2 from 3" h.r.s. channel.

You will need one for each door. They are made from a 28" long piece of 1/2" round rod. A metal lathe is used to turn the 3/8" diameter end 5-3/4" back from one end. The

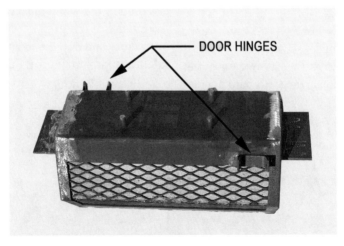

Figure 40. Photo showng locations of hinges on fire box.

42

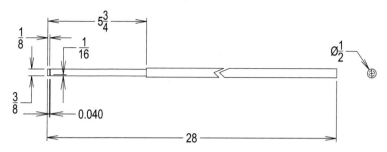

Figure 41. *Door rod blank. Make two from 1/2" diameter h.r.s. round rod.*

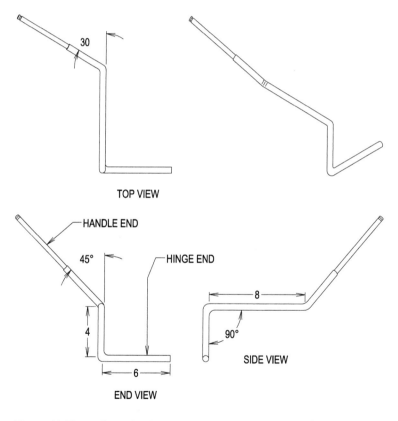

Figure 42. *Three views showing the bending angles for the door rods. Top right drawing is a perspective view after all bends have been made. Figure 45 shows the handle mounted on the door.*

43

lathe is also used to turn the .40 wide x 1/4" diameter groove required for the "e" clip that will be used to secure the wooden handle.

Details for the bending the door rods to fit the door and hinge are given in figure 42. You may use a flame torch to soften the areas of the rod where the bends are made, but a word of caution. As we blacksmiths say "don't touch deep recess in both ends to receive a 1" diameter washer. To achieve this, chuck up your chosen hardwood, turn the outside diameter, sand with garnet paper until smooth. Bore the 3/8" diameter hole through. Face to length. Make sure the wood is turning true or no wobbles as it turns. Use a 1" diameter forstner bit to drill 3/8" deep into both ends. Use a boring tool to slightly

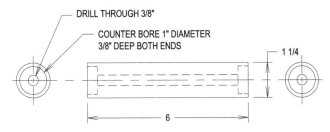

Figure 43. Wood handle detail. Make two from 1-1/4" diameter hardwood.

the hot part"! Heat and make your bends then use water to cool the metal before you touch it. Be safe! We used a short piece of 1" diameter pipe welded to a 6" x 6" x 3/8" thick steel plate clamped to one of my anvils. This provides a jig to bend metal around in a small radius.

The wood handles shown in figure 43 are of 1-1/4" dia. x 5" long hardwood with a 3/8" diameter hole bored through. There is a 1" diameter x 3/8" enlarge the diameter because the nominal size of the one inch washer is slightly bigger.

Try sizing by slipping on the wood handles, you just want the wood to turn but not sloppy. When satisfied with the fit, slide the wooden handle onto the metal rod with a 1" diameter washer on each end and secure with an "e" clip as shown in the figure 44.

Insert the rods into the door hinges to ensure the holes are large enough so that there is

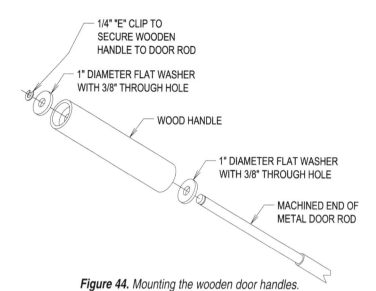

1/4" "E" CLIP TO
SECURE WOODEN
HANDLE TO DOOR ROD

1" DIAMETER FLAT WASHER
WITH 3/8" THROUGH HOLE

WOOD HANDLE

1" DIAMETER FLAT WASHER
WITH 3/8" THROUGH HOLE

MACHINED END OF
METAL DOOR ROD

Figure 44. Mounting the wooden door handles.

no binding as you turn the rod in the holes. Correct by slightly enlarging with a fractional drill bit if necessary.

Now you are ready to attach the door to the door rod. Place one of the finished doors over the opening at one end of the fire box. The cast refractory side facing to the inside and the metal side

Figure 45. Photo shows welds securing door rod to door facing.

facing out. Make sure the door covers the entire door opening. Insert the door rod into the door hinge. The 8" length between the first and second bends should be horizontal across the middle of the face of the door with the handle end toward you and on the left as you face the door.

With the door covering the door opening, make sure the rod is horizontal across the face of the door. When the door rod alignment is satisfactory, attach the rod to the door face with two 1" long weld beads equally spaced. Repeat the process for the other door. Clean and inspect. If the doors do not fit flush, adjust the bends until a

45

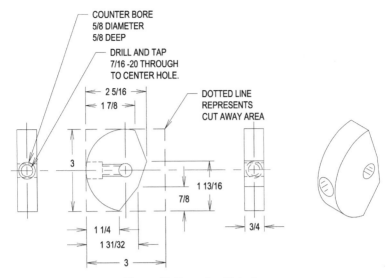

COUNTER BORE
5/8 DIAMETER
5/8 DEEP

DRILL AND TAP
7/16 -20 THROUGH
TO CENTER HOLE.

2 5/16
1 7/8

DOTTED LINE
REPRESENTS
CUT AWAY AREA

3

1 13/16

7/8

1 1/4
1 31/32
3

3/4

Figure 46. Door stop.Make two.

satisfactory fit is achieved. Now paint the door assemblies.

Now for the door hinge assembly. First you will need to make the door stop as shown in figure 46 from a 3" x 3" x 3/4" thick block of steel. To complete the door hinge assembly, you will need two compression springs, 2" long with a 1/2" through hole and the spring material being at least 1/8" diameter. You will also need two 1/8" x 1" roll pins and two flat washers

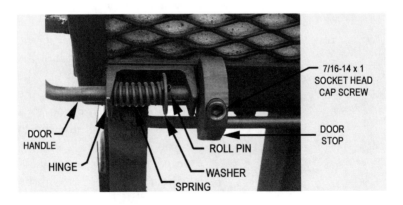

7/16-14 x 1
SOCKET HEAD
CAP SCREW

DOOR
STOP

DOOR
HANDLE

HINGE

ROLL PIN

WASHER

SPRING

Figure 47. Door hinge assembly detail.

Figure 48. *End view showing open doors.*

with 1/2" through holes. Refer to figure 47. Insert the spring onto the door rod within the door hinge ensuring that the door remains flush against the firebox. Slightly compress the spring toward the door end without moving anything else. Scribe a mark where the roll pin is to be drilled. Measure the diameter of the roll pins. You want to choose a drill bit about .005 thousands smaller than the actual measured pin. Remove the door rod and drill

for the roll pin. Reassemble the door assemblies, compress the spring and insert the roll pin, making sure the flat washer is between the spring and roll pin.

Next install the door stop adjusting it to allow the door to just clear the opening on each end as shown in figure 48. This may require grinding a bit off the edge of the door stop with a grinding wheel to achieve a proper fit.

Clean and paint. Watch the over spray.

Figure 49. *Typical analog pyrometer.*

Mounting the pyrometer

If you decide to use your forge as a heat treat oven, you will want to add a pyrometer. And, it's best to have the pyrometer in hand before beginning this part of the project as the size and hole locations of the mounting bracket and thermocouple

housing will be determined by actual measurements taken from your pyrometer and thermocouple.

We will begin by making and mounting the thermocouple housing. Its purpose is to protect the ceramic end of the

Figure 50. *12" long thermocouple.*

thermocouple. A photo of a typical thermocouple can be seen in figure 50. This particular one has a 12" probe and the ceramic block where the wire connections are made measures 1-1/4" wide x 7/8" tall x 1-1/4" long.

We used 1-1/2" x 1-1/2" x 1/8" square wall tubing for the housing. The inside measurements for this tubing are 1-1/4" x 1-1/4" which is ideal. The details for making the thermo-couple housing can be seen in figure 51. As you can see, the length of the tubing is 2-1/2" long. The 1/2" hole drilled

in one side gives an access point for the wire that will connect the thermocouple to the meter. The 1/4-20 tapped hole is for a set screw the purpose of which is to secure the ceramic end of the probe in the housing.

You can use a jig to locate the exact mounting position of the thermocouple housing to the end of the fire box. Such a jig is made from a piece of 3/4" x 1-1/4" steel 2" long. The jig detail is shown in figure 52 and the procedure for mounting the thermocouple housing is shown in figure 53. When positioned, secure the

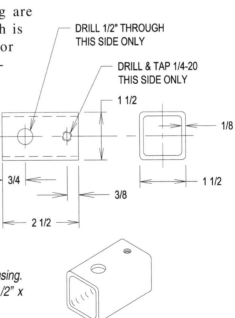

DRILL 1/2" THROUGH
THIS SIDE ONLY

DRILL & TAP 1/4-20
THIS SIDE ONLY

1 1/2

1/8

3/4

3/8

1 1/2

2 1/2

Figure 51. *Thermocouple housing. Make one from 1-1/2" x 1-1/2" x 1/8" wall square tubing.*

48

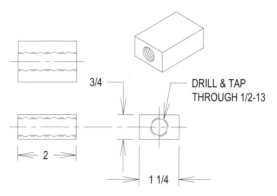

Figure 52. Jig for positioning thermocouple housing on the fire box end plate.

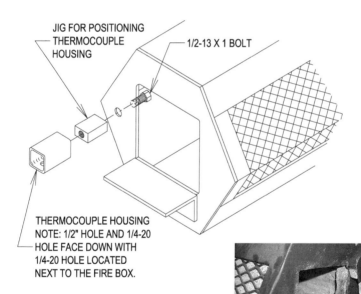

Figure 53. Mounting procedure for the thermocouple housing.

Figure 54. Thermocouple housing welded in place.

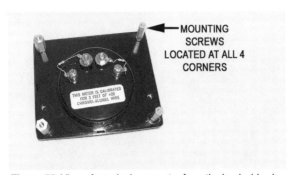

MOUNTING
SCREWS
LOCATED AT ALL 4
CORNERS

Figure 55. View of a typical pyrometer from the back side showing locations of the mounting screws.

housing with a tack weld on all four sides.

Now for the construction of the meter housing. Here again you need to measure the actual meter that you purchase to determine the mounting dimensions.

We were able to use hot rolled channel to house our meter, the detail of which is shown in figure 56. Begin by locating the mounting screw holes on the back of the meter. See figure 55. Transfer the location of the holes to the

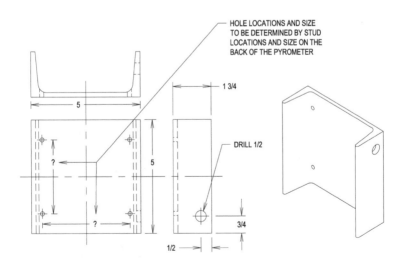

HOLE LOCATIONS AND SIZE
TO BE DETERMINED BY STUD
LOCATIONS AND SIZE ON THE
BACK OF THE PYROMETER

5

1 3/4

5

DRILL 1/2

?

?

1/2

3/4

Figure 56. Pyrometer housing. Size and hole locations to be determined by the pyrometer used.

50

metal housing. Drill clearance holes as shown. In the right side, and in the approximate location shown in the drawing, drill a 1/2" hole for wire access. When complete, weld the meter housing to the bottom of the fire box on the opposite end from the thermocouple housing. See figure 57.

Now would be a good time to place the fire box on the column. It will be heavy so get help for this job. Align the

Figure 57. View showing the pyrometer housing welded to the bottom of the fire box. Note thermocouple wire on right side.

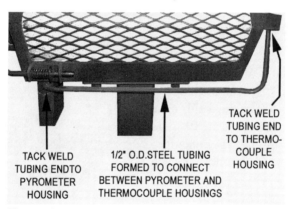

TACK WELD TUBING ENDTO PYROMETER HOUSING

1/2" O.D.STEEL TUBING FORMED TO CONNECT BETWEEN PYROMETER AND THERMOCOUPLE HOUSINGS

TACK WELD TUBING END TO THERMO-COUPLE HOUSING

Figure 58.

5/8" stud bolts in the bottom of the fire box with the holes in the top plate. Set the fire box in position and secure with nuts and lock washers.

It will be necessary to run wire from the thermocouple to the pyrometer and it would be best to enclose that wire in conduit. 1/2" O.D steel tubing will work well for this. You will need a piece about 30" long. Use a tube bender to bend to the desired shape as shown in figure 58. Then tack weld one end centered in the 1/2" hole in the pyrometer housing and tack weld the

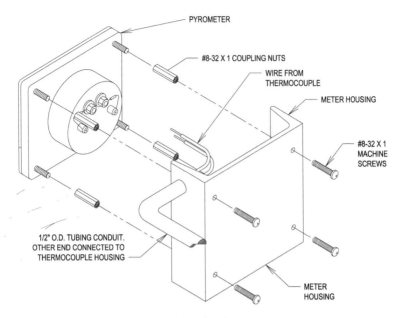

PYROMETER

#8-32 X 1 COUPLING NUTS

WIRE FROM
THERMOCOUPLE

METER HOUSING

#8-32 X 1
MACHINE
SCREWS

1/2" O.D. TUBING CONDUIT.
OTHER END CONNECTED TO
THERMOCOUPLE HOUSING

METER
HOUSING

Figure 59. *Mounting the pyrometer.*

other end centered in the 1/2"
hole in the thermocouple
housing. When the welds have
cooled, go ahead and thread
the wire through the conduit so
that about 2" extends out each
end.

Now mount the pyrometer
as shown in figure 59. Your
pyrometer may have different
mounting requirements so you
may have to devise other
methods, but even so, the
figure should give you a rough
idea of what you need to do.

Now wire and install the
thermocouple as shown in
figure 61. Once again, your
thermocouple may be

Figure 60. *View from the side showing pyrometer as it appears when installed.*

different from what is shown
in the drawing so different
mounting methods may need
to be devised.

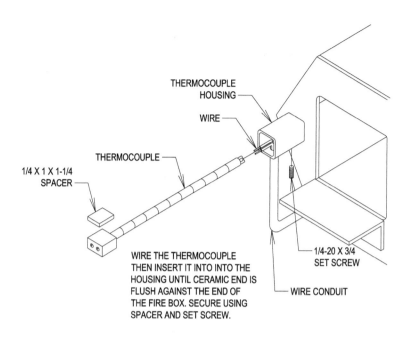

THERMOCOUPLE
HOUSING

WIRE

THERMOCOUPLE

1/4 X 1 X 1-1/4
SPACER

WIRE THE THERMOCOUPLE
THEN INSERT IT INTO INTO THE
HOUSING UNTIL CERAMIC END IS
FLUSH AGAINST THE END OF
THE FIRE BOX. SECURE USING
SPACER AND SET SCREW.

1/4-20 X 3/4
SET SCREW

WIRE CONDUIT

Figure 61. Installing the thermocouple.

The Manifold

The manifold is the heart of the forge. It uses atmospheric air with a venturi effect much like your car's carburetor. It is really quite simple but extremely effective. Inside the manifold head is a small hole drilled and directed down the nozzle. The pressure of the gas and the direction of the fuel cause atmospheric air to be pulled into the manifold head and mixed with the propane fuel before igniting. This is enough pressure to keep the flame below the nozzles within the firebox. However, should you experience burning within the copper nozzles, shut off fuel immediately wait a few

Figure 62. Rear view of manifold.

Figure 63. *Front view of manifold.*

seconds and relight. If the problem continues you may have a low propane fuel cylinder. Bob and I have made purchases of propane fuel tanks only to find out the tanks were nearly empty when told the tanks were newly filled. Make sure at time of purchase!

With the exception of the brace plate and manifold base plate, the manifold is an assembly of copper fittings. Earlier designs of the manifold were made of steel, but the copper fittings are available as standard size and there is less machining to do.

Notice the 3/8" diameter holes around the perimeter of the copper head as shown in the photos in figures 62 & 63. These holes allow for increased air flow and they enhance the air's ability to mix with the fuel. Strangely enough, these holes make the manifold act as if it is even bigger than it is. Through experimentation, we have found that going to larger diameter holes will not work well. And if the holes are absent, the forge will act as if it is starved for air.

Begin by making the brace plate as shown in figure 64 from a 2" x 6-3/4" piece of 3/16" h.r.s.. Drill the two 1-1/8" holes as shown taking care to locate them exactly 3-3/4" apart.

Make the base plate shown in figure 65 next from a 3-1/2" x 7" piece of 3/16"

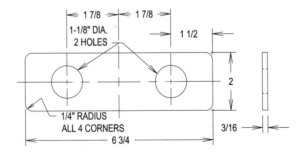

Figure 64. *Brace plate. Make 1 from a 2" x 6-3/4" piece of 3/16" thick h.r.s..*

54

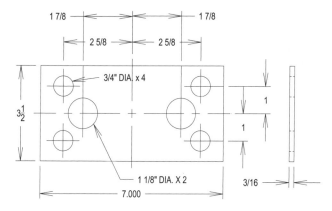

Figure 65. *Base plate. Make one from a 3-1/2" x 7" piece of 3/16" thick h.r.s..*

h.r.s.. Drill the four 3/4" vent holes and the two 1-1/8" holes as shown in the drawing. These holes can be cut with a holesaw at slow speed and lots of oil. Also, the holes must align with similar holes in the fire box top later so take special care to locate and drill them in the locations specified in the drawing.

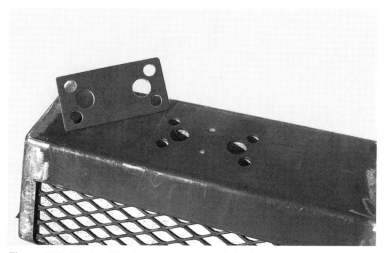

Figure 67A. *Photo of the base plate on top of the fire box to show correlation between holes in base plate and holes in top of fire box. It is important that these holes align or problems will result later when the manifold assembly is installed.*

Figure 66. A photo of the brace plate.

Figure 67. Photo of the base plate.

Now we will prepare the individual parts for, and assemble the manifold.

The manifold heads are made by drilling holes as shown figure 68 in one end of a 2" copper union. You will need to make two manifold heads. The 1/2" hole drilled through on center, 3/4" back from one end is simple to locate and drill so no discussion is needed. But the ten 3/8" holes equally spaced around the circumference present more of a challenge. This could be done by indexing using a dividing head and rotary table, but most of

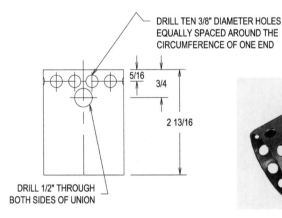

DRILL TEN 3/8" DIAMETER HOLES
EQUALLY SPACED AROUND THE
CIRCUMFERENCE OF ONE END

5/16

3/4

2 13/16

DRILL 1/2" THROUGH
BOTH SIDES OF UNION

2 1/4" DIAMETER

Figure 68. Manifold head. See figure 69 and text for details on how to locate the 3/8" holes around the circumference.

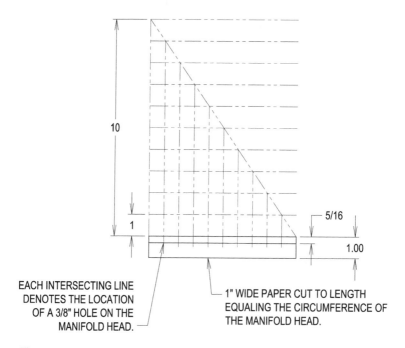

10

1

5/16

1.00

EACH INTERSECTING LINE
DENOTES THE LOCATION
OF A 3/8" HOLE ON THE
MANIFOLD HEAD.

1" WIDE PAPER CUT TO LENGTH
EQUALING THE CIRCUMFERENCE OF
THE MANIFOLD HEAD.

Figure 69. Using parallel lines to locate the 3/8" holes around circumference of
the manifold head. See text for further discussion on the process.

us do not have that capability. Not to worry, because the same job can be accomplished using a layout procedure called parallel line development. The procedure is as follows. . .

Begin by cutting a strip of construction paper 1" wide and at least long enough to wrap around the end of the 2" union leaving an overlap. Next wrap the 1" wide length of paper snugly around the rim of the union and secure it with removable tape. Cut through the overlap with a very keen knife and the length of the strip will now be the exact circumference of the copper union.

To divide the strip you will need a smooth board with a smooth straight edge, a clean sheet of 8-1/2 x 11 paper, a T-square and an accurate rule. Begin by placing a sheet of paper on the board. Square the edges and when square, tape the paper to the board.

We begin by drawing a straight line on the paper that is longer than the rim strip. Align the edge of the rim strip with this line and secure it to

57

the paper with removable tape. Now measure 5/16" down from the top edge of the rim strip and draw a straight line. Next raise a straight line 10" high from the top left corner of the rim strip as shown in figure 69. Next, draw a diagonal line from the top of the 10" line to the top right corner of the rim strip. Carefully divide the 10" line into 1" segments, then draw straight lines from each division to intersect with the diagonal line. Then drop perpendicular lines from the diagonal intersects to intersect with the line drawn on the rim strip 5/16" from its top edge. Each intersection will be the location for a 3/8" hole with the tenth hole being located at that point where the ends of rim strip meet when rewrapped around the union. So with that in mind, rewrap the rim strip around the rim of the union and secure it with tape. The rim strip should fit snugly and the ends should butt up evenly with each other. Before drilling, mark the location of each hole with a center punch. Secure the union in a vise and proceed to step drill the holes to 3/8" diameter. Step drilling means starting with a small

drill, for instance 1/8", and then gradually increasing drill sizes until the required diameter is met. In this instance 3/8".

We are ready to assemble the manifold. The assembly will consist of the base and brace plates that we made earlier, two manifold heads, two 2" to 1" copper reducers as shown in the right side of the photo in figure 70 and finally four 1" I.D. x 3" long pieces of copper tubing. We will need a number of jigs and fixtures to accurately assemble the manifold and these will be discussed as they are needed.

First assemble the manifold heads and the 2" x 1" copper reducers. You will need an alignment fixture for this procedure and you can make such a fixture from a 1-1/2" diameter wooden dowel 3" long. One end of the dowel is

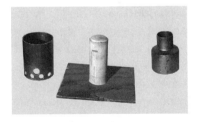

Figure 70. *The alignment jig in the center is used to assemble the manifold head on the left and the 2" x 1" copper reducer on the right.*

58

Figure 71. Place the manifold on the jig as shown with the end with the drilled holes facing down.

Figure 72. Insert the copper reducer as shown. The wood dowel prevents the reducer from going too far into the manifold head.

rounded concave and the other end is flat. The flat end is fastened to a wood base with a wood screw. See photo in figure 70. The copper union is placed over the wood dowel with the end with the drilled holes facing down. The reducer is inserted into the union and the wood dowel causes the reducer to come to a predetermined positive stop. At this point both the manifold

Figure 73. The dimple tool consists of two pieces of hardwood cut to the general shape shown. The pieces are held together with nuts and bolts. The center hole is sized to fit the diameter of pipe being worked with. A bolt with point turned on its end is threaded into the top of the dimple tool.

Figure 74. A close up of the pointed end on the bolt discribed in figure 73.

Figure 75. Here we see the dimple tool in use. As the center bolt is tightened, the pointed end puts a dimple impression in the two interlocking pieces which prevents them from coming apart.

head and the copper reducer need to be either soldered together or we developed another method in which the fittings could be secured and we refer to that method as dimpling. See figures 73 through 75. The basic idea of the dimple tool is that a clamp similar to a flaring clamp is placed around the copper connection. A bolt with a point machined on its end is threaded into the copper forcing it in just enough to slightly deform or dimple the two interlocking pieces. The dimple prevents the pieces from moving or pulling apart. We still recommend soldering the copper pieces later but while assembling this process is wonderful! Note though, that the tool is only good for

the diameter tubing it is made for.

Align the 1/2" through holes in both manifold heads with an 8" length of 1/2" O.D. copper tubing as shown in figure 76. The alignment tube will be removed later so do not solder it. Next insert the 3" long piece of 1" copper pipe into the reducer end as shown. Adjust the 1" copper pipe so that 2-1/8" extends past the edge of the reducer lip as shown in figure 77. Then dimple and solder the connection. After soldering, slide the brace plate over both 1" tubes and position it flush against the reducer lip. Solder

Figure 76. Align the 1/2" through holes in both manifold heads with an 8" length of 1/2" O.D. copper tubing. The 1/2" copper tube is for aligning purposes only so do not solder. Next, insert a 3" length of 1" copper tube into each manifold head as shown.

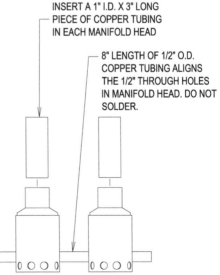

INSERT A 1" I.D. X 3" LONG PIECE OF COPPER TUBING IN EACH MANIFOLD HEAD

8" LENGTH OF 1/2" O.D. COPPER TUBING ALIGNS THE 1/2" THROUGH HOLES IN MANIFOLD HEAD. DO NOT SOLDER.

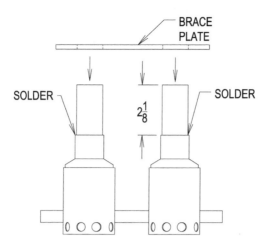

Figure 77. *Adjust the 1" copper tube so that 2-1/8" extends past the reducer lip. Then solder the connection. After soldering, slide the brace plate on the copper tubes as shown.*

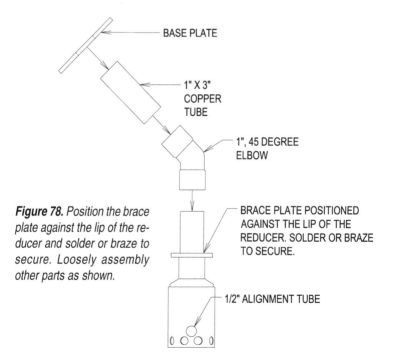

Figure 78. *Position the brace plate against the lip of the reducer and solder or braze to secure. Loosely assembly other parts as shown.*

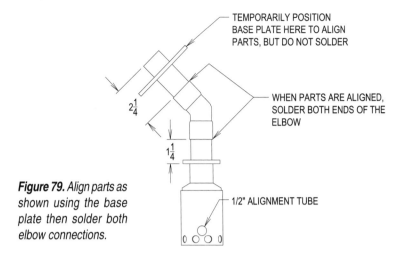

TEMPORARILY POSITION
BASE PLATE HERE TO ALIGN
PARTS, BUT DO NOT SOLDER

$2\frac{1}{4}$

WHEN PARTS ARE ALIGNED,
SOLDER BOTH ENDS OF THE
ELBOW

$1\frac{1}{4}$

1/2" ALIGNMENT TUBE

Figure 79. Align parts as shown using the base plate then solder both elbow connections.

or braze to secure as shown in figure 78.

Loosely assemble the 45 degree elbows, the additional 3" lengths of 1" pipe and the base plate as shown in figure 78. Adjust and align as shown in figure 79. When satisfied with the assembly, solder the connections at both ends of the 45 degree elbows. Finally, position the base plate flush against the lip of the 45 degree elbow as shown in figure 80 and solder or braze to secure.

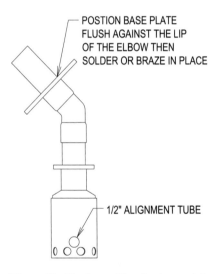

POSTION BASE PLATE
FLUSH AGAINST THE LIP
OF THE ELBOW THEN
SOLDER OR BRAZE IN PLACE

1/2" ALIGNMENT TUBE

Figure 80. Finally, position the base plate flush against the lip of the elbow and solder or braze to secure.

The fuel line

At this point we are ready to make the fuel line. There are a few things to consider. This really is your choice as you could use a shorter fuel line and have a valve near the from a 48" length of 1/2" O.D. copper or steel tubing. Layout the location for the orifice holes and the witness mark. You must mark these three locations on the same plane.

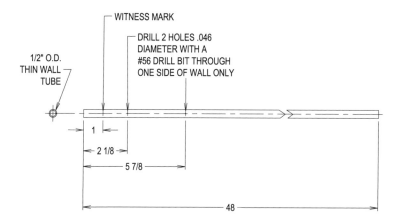

Figure 81. *The fuel line. Make one from 1/2" O.D. copper tubing or 1/2" O.D. thin wall steel tubing.*

manifold head or could continue as detailed here and make the fuel line longer with the shut off valve located on the column under the fire box. The advantage of a longer fuel line is that fewer connections are required, but on the downside, making the bends will be a bit more of a challenge

The fuel line layout is shown in figure 81. It is made Layout as follows. Place the fuel line in a vise, gently, and position it close to the top of the vise horizontally and allow one end to extend slightly out one side of the vise. Make sure the fuel line cannot roll in the vise nor crush. Do not remove the fuel line from the vise until all of the following procedure is completed. From the short end extending out from the end of the vise,

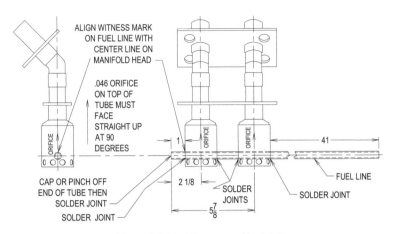

ALIGN WITNESS MARK ON FUEL LINE WITH CENTER LINE ON MANIFOLD HEAD

.046 ORIFICE ON TOP OF TUBE MUST FACE STRAIGHT UP AT 90 DEGREES

ORIFICE

CAP OR PINCH OFF END OF TUBE THEN SOLDER JOINT

SOLDER JOINT

1

ORIFICE

ORIFICE

41

2 1/8

$5\frac{7}{8}$

SOLDER JOINTS

FUEL LINE

SOLDER JOINT

Figure 82. Fuel line assembly detail.

measure 1" and mark center. This first mark is a witness mark and will be used to position the tubing in the manifold head later. Next measure 2-1/8" from the same end and mark center for the location of the first orifice hole. Now measure 5-7/8" from the same end to locate and mark center for the second orifice hole. As mentioned earlier it is important that all of the above locations be aligned and drilled on center. So it would be best to complete the drilling operation by mounting the vise on a mill/drill table. That way the hole locations will remain on the same plane as you crank the table to the next hole location.

So to begin the drilling operation, mount the vise

holding the fuel line on a mill drill table. At the witness mark located 1" from the end, scribe a line to locate center.

Then move the table forward to the 2-1/8" mark. When positioned on center, drill a .046" hole with a number 56 drill bit. **Drill only through one wall of the fuel line.**

Now raise the drill and move forward to the 5-7/8" mark. When positioned, drill another .046" orifice hole with a #56 drill through one wall of the fuel line. Blow air through the line to clean away dirt and metal chips.

Now the prepared fuel line is ready to be inserted into the manifold heads. The important thing is that the orifice be pointed in correct direction as

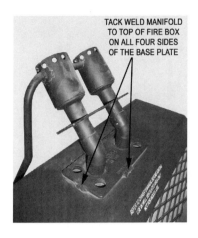

TACK WELD MANIFOLD
TO TOP OF FIRE BOX
ON ALL FOUR SIDES
OF THE BASE PLATE

Figure 83. Position manifold on top of fire box as discribed in the text. Then tack weld on four sides of base plate as shown in the photo.

indicated in the drawing in figure 82. The manifold should be positioned on a flat surface with the hole end facing down. Insert the tubing into and through the 1/2" holes in the manifold heads so that approximately 1" extends out one end as shown. Align the witness mark on the fuel line with the witness mark on the manifold head. Ensure orifices are facing in the right direction aimed straight down the 1" tubing. When satisfied that the fuel line is oriented properly, solder four

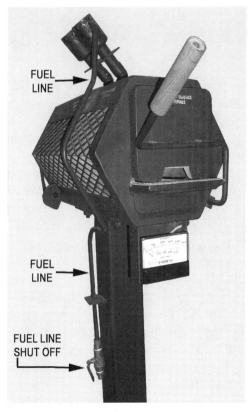

FUEL LINE

FUEL LINE

FUEL LINE SHUT OFF

Figure 84. Side view showing fuel line bends and fuel shut off valve.

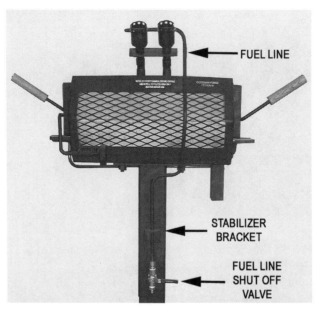

Figure 85. *Front view showing fuel line bends and position of fuel line stabilizer bracket.*

Figure 86. *Typical coil type tube bender.*

joints as indicated in the drawing. Pinch or cap off the short end of the tubing and seal the end with solder. We used silver solder as it is stronger weld joint.

The next step is to position the manifold on top of the fire box as shown in figure 83. The required bends in the fuel line can either be made before mounting the manifold or after the fact. At any rate, to mount the manifold, align the vent holes in the base plate with the vent holes in the fire box top. The copper nozzles should mate with their respective holes in the top of the fire box as well. Each copper nozzle should extend inside of the fire box at least one inch below the refractory. If the vent holes line up between the manifold base plate and the top of the firebox plate vent holes then you are in business and you

66

can tack weld the manifold base plate to the top of the firebox.

A detailed description of the bend angles proved confusing so we felt it best to rely on photos in figures 84 and 85 for direction. Essentially, the bends position the fuel line about 1" from the surface of the fire box, and beginning with the 90 degree bend straight down at the manifold, they follow the contour of the fire box. Then a 90 degree bend is made at the bottom of the fire box to bring the fuel line to the center of the column. Then another 90 degree bend directs the line down the length of the column as can be seen in the photo. It is best to use a tubing bender for the bending process or kinks will result. A coiled spring bender as shown in the photo in figure 86 is available at most hardware stores and delivers excellent results.

Make the fuel line stabilizer bracket from a piece of 3" x 3" x 1/8" angle iron 3-3/4" long as shown in figure

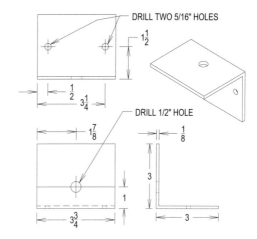

Figure 87. Stabilizer bracket detail.

87. Drill the 1/2" hole in one leg of the angle as shown and the two 5/16" holes in the other leg. To mount the stabilizer bracket, slide the 1/2" diameter fuel line into the 1/2" hole of the bracket. Slide the bracket up to approximately 9" below the bottom edge of the fire box. Center the bracket on the column, then transfer the locations of the two 5/16" holes in the bracket to the column using a transfer punch. Remove the bracket to drill and tap two 1/4-20 holes at the marked locations. Then reposition the bracket and secure it to the column with 1/4-20 bolts. The stabilizer bracket could be welded to the column instead,

Figure 88. The fuel tank is connected, and the forge is ready to go. This is the set up if you intend to use the unit as a forge. See figure 91 to set the unit up as a heat treat oven.

but if that is done it would be difficult to disassemble the unit without cutting the fuel line.

Finally, install a shut off valve at the end of the fuel line using a compression fitting or a flare fitting would work as well.

If you plan to use the unit as a forge only, attach an 18" flexible LP gas line to the other side of the shut off valve and connect it to a regulator valve at the LP gas tank. Use the same type of regulator that you would use on your barbecue grill. See figure 88.

After a final check for leaks, you're ready to work!

If on the other hand, you want to use the unit as a heat treat oven, you will need to set things up a bit different. Instead of a fixed regulator, you will want to install one that is adjustable along with a pressure gage.

A photo showing a typical adjustable gas regulator is shown in figure 89. This one being adjustable from 0-15 pounds pressure, but one that is adjustable from 0-10 pounds would be adequate. The regulator will have an in port and an out port as well as a port for connecting a pressure gage. This particular regulator is made by Rego and is listed as part # 597FA. Gas regulators such as these can be purchased from just about any gas supply dealer and at the time this book went to press the cost was in the $25.00 to $30.00 range.

You will also need a pressure gage such as the one shown in figure 90 and you should be able to purchase it at the same place you purchase your regulator.

The regulator and gage as they appear connected to the propane tank are shown in figure 91. It is a simple matter to connect using copper tubing and flare fittings.

Using the adjustable regulator and pressure gage in conjunction with the pyrometer will allow you to stabilize the heat inside the oven and achieve consistent and accurate temperatures for your heat treating projects.

Figure 89. The adjustable regulator.

Figure 90. Typical pressure gage.

Figure 91. This is the set up if you intend to use the unit as a heat treat oven.

Final assembly

To test the Forge, make sure all the fittings are tight. To test for leaks, use soapy water with the line valve closed and tank valve open. Apply soapy water to the line, if bubbles appear, then a leak is needing to be repaired. Do so at this time.

Lighting the Forge is similar to lighting a gas grill. Safety glasses and welding gloves are used. Open the tank valve, adjust the regulator to about 1-1/2 pounds pressure, open the line valve, and light with a grill lighter. There will be a puff as fuel is ignited and that is normal. The flame should be clear to slightly blue and burning just below the copper nozzles. If the flame is yellow then the Forge is starving for air and you should back off the gas pressure. If there is a roar and you are unable to see the flame then the flame is burning inside the nozzles or in the manifold. In this instance, shut down immediately! There is not enough pressure or the fuel tank is low. Increase the pressure or refill the tank. We experienced two eight hour days of continuous burning with a 40 pound LP gas tank.

A beer bottle placed in the fire box before firing melted into a molten puddle in twenty seconds and temperatures reach 2500 degrees inside the firebox in about two minutes.

On your first firing of the forge, steam will develop after about 10 minutes as water is cooked out of the forge, this is normal so don't worry. We placed pumice or lava rock in the bottom to level the floor of the Forge and help retain heat around the work. Try not to block the thermocouple from the flame. Doing so would cause the pyrometer to record incorrect temperatures. Putting something between the flame and thermocouple only serves to give incorrect readings and may spoil any heat treatments you might do.

As you use the Forge, use all pertinent safety gear, eye protection, and gloves. Never leave the forge unattended while it is in operation. Watch the hot parts!, be safe, and have fun!

Conclusion

Well you did it! You built your own heat treating Atmospheric Forge. We went through and discussed the whys and wherefores, cut the metal, assembled the parts, mixed the refractory, looked at the drawings and photos, and figured out how to do all of this. Now you stand back, rub your back, and look at this creation before you. Have a cup of coffee or what ever you like. Not only have you built a forge, you have to a degree made yourself more independent. You have a tool to fashion other tools or even open a door to learn an old skill.

You have to admit, it's really something to look at. You can take it any where in the world and it still works. It doesn't need electricity, so that leash is gone. It gets to 2500 degrees in two minutes without a blower. By the pressure valve on the tank, you can control its temperature. Now you can forge work with it and heat treat metal. You're not dependant on other fuel sources.

The flame when working properly is clear with a blue tint. If you see a yellow flame then you have low pressure or you are about to run out of fuel. Remember, sometimes when you purchase fuel, the tank is not always full. Have fun, be safe. If you need parts to make the forge, our address is on page 12 of this book or write to the publisher. They will see we get the mail. Remember to send along a self addressed stamped envelope with all inquiries.

We have other projects we want to write about if you like this one. Treadle hammers, swage blocks, 14 inch band saws just as good looking as the factory and better quality, too. Dies for the hammers, a foundry furnace using our gas manifolds and more!

Thank you,

Wm. T. Goodman